Survival Kit for New Christians

Presented by _____

My Personal Journey:

Name _____

Place I became a Christian _____

Date I became a Christian _____

Date I was baptized into a church fellowship _____

Persons who helped me come to know Christ:

_____   _____

_____   _____

_____   _____

_____   _____

Date I began work in *Survival Kit for New Christians, Children's Edition*

_____

Date I completed work in *Survival Kit for New Christians, Children's Edition*

_____

Dewey Decimal Classification Number: J248.4
Subject Heading: CHRISTIAN LIFE/SALVATION
Printed in the United States of America
Item # 5131-73
ISBN # 0-8054-9601-7

Reprinted 1981, 1982, 1983, 1985, 1986, 1987, 1989, 1990, 1991, 1996

Children/Preschool Section
Youth/Children/Preschool Department
Discipleship and Family Development Division
The Sunday School Board of the Southern Baptist Convention

To order additional copies of this resource:
WRITE: Customer Service Center,
        127 Ninth Avenue, North,
        Nashville, TN 37234-0113;
FAX order to (615) 251-5933;
PHONE 1-800-458-2772;
EMAIL to CompuServe ID 70423,2526;
or visit the Baptist Book Store serving you.

All Scripture references are from the *Good News Bible,* The Bible in Today's English Version. Old Testament: Copyright © American Bible Society 1976; New Testament: Copyright © American Bible Society 1966, 1971, 1976. Used by permission.

Meet Jim and Janet . . .

Jim is older than Janet—20 minutes older. That's because they are *twins!*

But Janet is *spiritually* older than Jim—*nearly two weeks older.* You see, Janet gave the control of her life to Jesus almost two weeks before Jim made his decision to become a Christian.

Jim and Janet are more than twins. They are also *best friends*. Jim was surprised when Janet prayed alone with their mother, giving her life to Jesus. Jim said, "Janet, I thought we were going to become Christians *together*."

Janet replied: "No, Jim. Each one of us must trust Jesus for himself. You must make your own decision to trust Jesus. Then, we'll grow as Christians together."

"You're right, Janet," said Jim. "I know Jesus died for my sin, and no one else can ask him to forgive my sin but *me*."

Two weeks later, Mr. Robinson, Jim's Sunday School teacher, said: "Jim, have you invited Jesus to be ruler of your life? If not, would you like to do so now?"

Jim replied: "Thank you for asking me about this. I decided I wanted to give my life to Jesus several days ago." While his teacher listened, Jim prayed.

When he told Janet, her eyes sparkled with happiness. She said, "Now we can learn about this new life together."

WOULD YOU LIKE TO BE *BEST FRIENDS* WITH JIM AND JANET?

Walk along with them as they discover from the Bible how to grow as a new Christian. Spend ten minutes each day, five days each week, with this book. *But don't do more than one lesson a day.*

IMPORTANT: In the middle of this book, there are twelve Scripture Memory Cards to be cut out. Read the directions for using the cards. MEMORIZE TWO VERSES EACH WEEK.

At the end of weeks 2 through 6, there is a REVIEW. You should work through each REVIEW page with one of your parents. *PLEASE ASK YOUR PARENT TO READ PAGE 64 NOW.* Reading page 64 will help them know how to work with you.

Week 1: My new life
Day 1: Having a devotional time

Jim and Janet told their parents at once that Jim had prayed to invite Jesus to be his master. Dad said, "Jim, we are happy you have asked Jesus Christ to forgive your sin and to live in your life." Mother suggested they should begin to have daily devotional times each morning.

"What is a devotional time?" asked Janet.

Mother explained: "It's a time when you go to a special place to read your Bible and talk to God. During that time you think about the meaning of the Bible verses you read and ask God to help you live for Jesus that day."

"That's right," said Dad. "I began my devotional times when I was only eleven years old. I know you have often seen me studying my Bible in the mornings. That's my regular time to pray and read the Bible. Without it, I don't find it easy to live each day with the Lord Jesus in control. It is really important to have this special time each morning."

THE CENTER OF YOUR SURVIVAL KIT HAS TWO SECRET CODE CARDS. One is for you, and the other is for your *best friend.* You can use the code cards to send special messages to each other. Cut the cards to fit a billfold. **JIM AND JANET** will use theirs to send *you* secret messages. Follow the instructions on the back of the cards.

HERE'S YOUR FIRST MESSAGE! Can you decode it? (Write the alphabet letters beneath each number to get the message Jim and Janet want to send to you.)

2-14-5-14-21-11   26   20-5-26-21-14   11-15   10-26-9-14

_ _ _ _ _ _   _   _ _ _ _ _   _ _   _ _ _ _

19-15-25-16   12-14-9-15-11-22-15-13-26-5

_ _ _ _   _ _ _ _ _ _ _ _ _ _

11-22-18-14.

_ _ _ _.

Jim and Janet looked up the following Bible verses. What did they learn from the Bible about having a devotional time? (If you need

help in finding these verses, ask your parents to show you how to find them.)
Read PSALM 5:3.

A good time to meet and share with Jesus is in the

_ _ _ _ _ _ _ .

Read 1 PETER 2:2.

As new babies long for _ _ _ _ to drink, we should desire to read the Bible, so that we may grow in understanding of our new life in Christ.

MATCH THESE SENTENCES:

A GOOD DEVOTIONAL TIME IS   SPECIAL TIME AND PLACE FOR MY DEVOTIONAL TIME.

A "DEVOTIONAL TIME" IS WHEN   I READ MY BIBLE AND PRAY DAILY.

I SHOULD CHOOSE A   IN THE MORNING.

I WILL HAVE MY QUIET TIME . . .

AT THIS SPECIAL PLACE:_____
_____

AT THIS SPECIAL TIME:_____ A.M.

SIGNED:_____

Week 1: My new life
Day 2: How to find books in the Bible

Jim and Janet were eating ice cream bars and watching TV cartoons on Friday afternoon. The doorbell rang.

As usual, they raced each other to the door to see who could open it first. Mr. Robinson, Jim's Sunday School teacher, was smiling as they opened the door. "Hooray!" he said. "I was hoping I might find both of you at home. I have brought each of you a gift." Jim and Janet were pleased. They enjoyed getting presents.

Carefully, Mr. Robinson took from his Bible two identical pictures. He gave one to each of them and said: "This is a picture of a bookshelf full of books. It helped me learn that the Bible is not just one book but a whole library of books. I thought you might like to have a copy, too."

Janet looked at the picture carefully. "Oh, I see! All the books in our Bible are shown, but this picture makes it look like each one is a separate book from the others."

Jim said: "Janet, that's because they *are* all different books. The books are now together in one book, but the books were written by many different men. Some of them lived hundreds of years apart."

"I'm glad you have remembered our Sunday School lesson so well, Jim," said Mr. Robinson. "If you will look at this picture when you forget where Bible books are located, you will soon know how to find each one."

After Mr. Robinson left, Jim and Janet played a game with their new pictures. They took turns calling out the name of a Bible book. The other would try to tell in which division of the Bible the book is located without looking at the picture. They both did well with the New Testament. Jim had trouble with some of the books in the Minor Prophets. Janet won by three points. Jim promised her that the next time they played this game, he certainly would win! He went to his room and studied his new picture.

Can you write in the names of the missing books? To find the answers, look in the front of your own Bible for a list of the books in the Bible. If you need help, ask your parents to work with you.

SECRET MESSAGE FROM JIM AND JANET:

13-14-14-12   10-14-5-20?   5-15-15-24   22-13

_ _ _ _   _ _ _ _   _ _ _ _   _ _

11-10-14   3-16-15-13-11   15-3   19-15-25-16

_ _ _   _ _ _ _ _   _ _   _ _ _ _

8-22-8-5-14.   26-5-5   8-15-15-24-2   26-16-14

_ _ _ _ _.   _ _ _   _ _ _ _ _ _   _ _ _

5-22-2-11-14-12   11-10-14-16-14.

_ _ _ _ _ _ _   _ _ _ _ _.

Can you remember Psalm 119:11? If so, repeat it aloud.

Why is the Bible special? Find the answer in 2 Peter 1:21 and

write your answer here:_____

_____

_____

_____

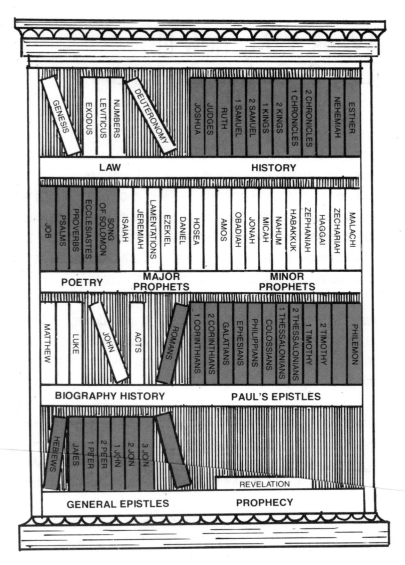

Week 1: My new life
Day 3: Scripture memory

Janet carefully arranged her Scripture memory cards in her billfold. After Jim had given the billfold to her for Christmas, she had put pictures of actors she watched on TV in each of the plastic windows. As Jim entered the room, he saw her changing the pictures for Scripture memory cards. He said: "2 Corinthians 5:17 is true! 'The old is gone, the new has come.' You are changing those silly pictures in your billfold for Scripture memory cards."

Janet replied: "Well, this way I can look at them during lunch hour at school, and they won't get dirty—like *your* memory verse cards will, Jim. Honestly, I think boys will never learn to take care of things they own."

Jim smiled. Janet always teased him about not keeping his room neat or his shirt tucked in. "Look!" he said. "I have made a special holder for my cards. This will keep them clean." He showed Janet a folder he had made from a piece of heavy paper. "Memorizing the verses is more important than how we carry them. When we need the verses, we will know them. Scripture verses we have memorized will be our 'secret weapons' when temptations come."

A SECRET MESSAGE TO YOU FROM JIM AND JANET:

23-15-25-5-12   19-15-25   5-22-24-14   11-15

— — — — — — — — — — — — — —

18-26-24-14   26   10-15-5-12-14-16   3-15-16

— — — — — — — — — — — — — —

19-15-25-16   21-26-16-12-2?   3-15-5-5-15-23

— — — — — — — — — — — — — — —

20-5-26-13   2-10-15-23-13.

— — — — — — — — —.

TRACE THE FOLLOWING DIAGRAM ON HEAVY PAPER, US-
ING TRACING PAPER. CUT OUT AND GLUE TOGETHER.

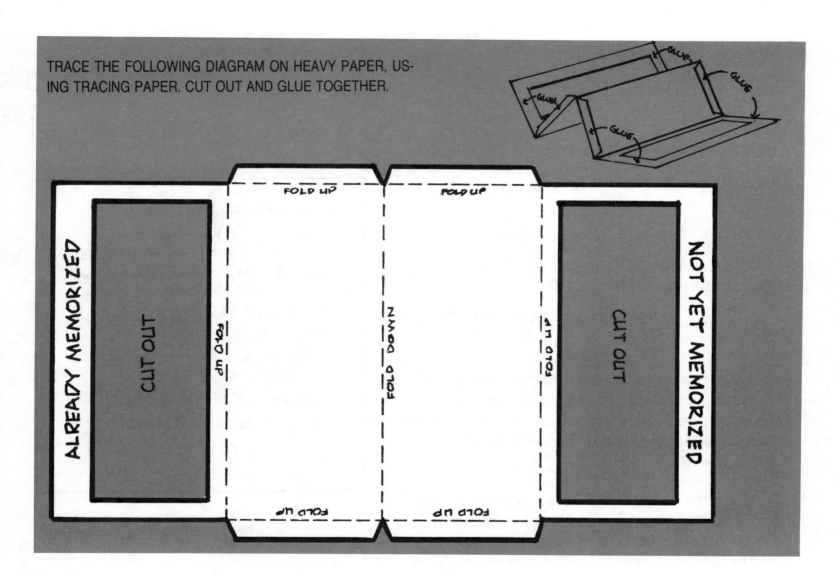

Week 1: My new life
Day 4: How to pray

SECRET MESSAGE FROM JIM AND JANET:

8-14-3-15-16-14   19-15-25   16-14-26-12

_ _ _ _ _ _   _ _ _   _ _ _ _

2-11-15-16-19,   5-15-15-24   25-20   11-10-14-2-14

_ _ _ _ _   _ _ _ _   _ _   _ _ _ _ _

2-21-16-22-20-11-25-16-14-2:

_ _ _ _ _ _ _ _ _ _: COLOSSIANS 4:2 and MATTHEW 7:7.

Jim and Janet sat on the front row in the church sanctuary. Mr. Robinson had encouraged Jim to take notes while the pastor preached, and Janet also decided to do so. Pastor Beall was an interesting speaker and told many stories that helped Jim and Janet understand his sermon.

Sitting with them was Jim's friend, Richard. He also had recently become a Christian. However, neither Richard's mother or brother ever attended church. (His father no longer lived with them.) It was much harder for him to grow as a Christian, for he did not get much

encouragement at home. Jim felt a real desire to help him. "Richard," whispered Jim, "the pastor is going to speak about prayer today. We'll compare notes when the service is over."

After the worship service, Jim's notes looked like this:

1. Prayer is talking to God.
   Colossians 4:2: We should pray often.
                    We can thank God for his help.
   Matthew 7:7: God wants us to ask him to guide us.
                    He is happy when we do so.
2. People in the Bible who prayed.
   JESUS: Prayed all night.
   PAUL: Prayed in prison.
   DISCIPLES: Prayed often.
   Mother of SAMUEL: Prayed for a baby.
3. Things we should pray about.
   ? ? ? ?

Richard and Janet looked at Jim's notes. Richard said: "Jim, why did you put question marks after Pastor Beall's last point? He gave us a list of things to pray about. See? Look at my list." Richard had written:

Pray for missionaries   Pray for our government
Pray for sick people   Pray for salvation of others

Jim said: "Yes, I know he said to pray for those things. But Pastor Beall also said to pray for people *by name.* I decided to use my devotional time to write down my own *special list of names* for my prayer time."

Sadly, Richard said: "Jim and Janet, when you write down your list of unbelievers, would you add the names of my dad and mother and brother? How I wish they would accept Jesus as Lord as we have done!"

"Yes," said Jim. "You can count on us. We'll pray *every day* for them. Let's also pray for George. His parents argue and fight a lot. I don't think his mother feels good. Let's pray that they will accept Jesus as Lord soon." Jim continued: "Do you understand now why I put question marks in my notes of Pastor Beall's sermon? I wanted to pray about *real* people and *real* problems. That is when prayer becomes important!"

HERE'S A PRAYER LIST FOR YOU!

What would you like to pray for in your devotional time? Add to this in the days to come. Use it regularly. *Always close your devotional time with prayer.*

My Prayer List			
Name	Problem	Date I Began to Pray	Date God Answered My Prayer

Week 1: My new life
Day 5: My first Bible study

What have you done in the past that makes you know you are?

_____

_____

A SECRET MESSAGE FROM JIM AND JANET:

11-10-22-2   8-22-8-5-14   2-11-25-12-19   10-14-5-20-14-12

_ _ _ _   _ _ _ _ _   _ _ _ _ _   _ _ _ _ _ _

25-2.   23-14   24-13-15-23   19-15-25   23-22-5-5

_ _   _ _   _ _ _ _   _ _ _   _ _ _ _

5-22-24-14   22-11,   11-15-15!

_ _ _ _   _ _   _ _ _!

MY QUIET TIME FOR   _____ _____ _____

                              month   day   year

1. BIBLE STUDY
READ 1 TIMOTHY 1:15
Why did Christ Jesus come into the world?

To S _ _ _   S _ _ _ _ _ _ _.
According to this verse, are *you* one? ☐ YES ☐ NO

Here is an apple tree. Why do we call it *apple*?
Because it grows apples. When it is wintertime, are there *apples* on the tree? ☐ YES ☐ No
What name do we call the tree when there are *no* apples on it?

_____

(Answer: Apple)

We call it by the same name, whether it has apples on it or not, *because it is an apple tree by nature.*

WE CALL THE TREE *APPLE* BECAUSE OF ITS *NATURE.*
WE CALL THE FRUIT *APPLES* BECAUSE THEY CAME FROM THE *APPLE TREE.*

Some people confuse SIN with SINS. SIN is rebelling against God. Sin is wanting my way instead of God's way. Rebellion against God is the NATURE of all people who are not Christians. SINS are the fruit of that rebellion. Things like cheating, fussing, stealing, and mistreating people are SINS.

IN THE LIST BELOW, UNDERLINE WORDS THAT DESCRIBE *SINS*, NOT *SIN*:

Stealing candy	Disobeying parents
Cheating on a test	Wanting my way instead of God's way

CAN YOU MATCH THE RIGHT PARTS OF THESE PHRASES TO MAKE SENTENCES?

Sin is   the fruit (actions or deeds) of desiring to disobey God

Sins are   choosing to follow your way instead of God's

WRITE PSALM 119:11 FROM MEMORY:_____

_____

_____

_____

_____

_____

WRITE 2 CORINTHIANS 5:17 FROM MEMORY:_____

_____

_____

_____

_____

_____

Week 2: One body
Day 1: Five things to learn

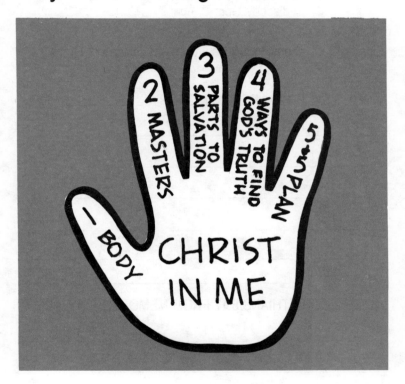

Janet and Jim knocked on Pastor Beall's office door. It was the first time they had been inside his office. His well-worn Bible was open on his desk. As they entered, he said: "I'm *glad* you have come to talk with me. While I waited for our appointment, I have been having a special devotional time."

Janet said: "Pastor Beall, why do *you* need to have devotional times? You already know so much about the Bible. You have even been to the seminary to study it. I thought devotional times are for people who are *new* Christians."

"Oh, no, Janet," said Pastor Beall. "I need to let Jesus teach me from the Scriptures every day. Why, many of my sermons are the result of what the Lord teaches me about myself in my devotional times."

As the twins sat down, Pastor Beall reached for a picture he had placed on his desk. "Did you know I like to draw illustrations?" Smiling, he continued, "I *can* do other things in addition to preaching sermons, you know!" He handed them the drawing he had made. "This is a hand. On the fingers, I have written five things for you to remember. On the palm I have written, CHRIST IN ME to show that Jesus has come to live in my life." He pointed to the thumb and said: "The thumb reminds me that Jesus has ONE BODY—and we call that body his *church.* Jim and Janet, you are now members of that body. You accepted Jesus as your Master, and the moment you did so, he added you to his body."

FIND AND READ 1 CORINTHIANS 12:12,18 IN YOUR BIBLE.

Pastor Beall asked Jim to read 1 Corinthians 12:12,18. When Jim finished reading, the pastor gave each of them a copy of the puzzle he had drawn. Both Jim and Janet enjoyed finishing their puzzles.

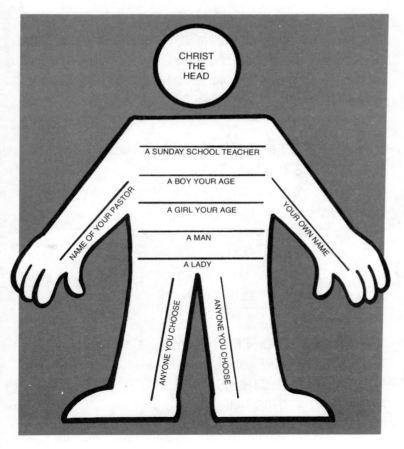

WOULD YOU LIKE TO FINISH THE PUZZLE, TOO? In the blanks write names of people who are members of the church you attend.

According to 1 Corinthians 12:18, how are we placed in the body, the church?

_____

_____

_____

_____

_____

SECRET MESSAGE FROM JIM AND JANET

16-14-9-22-14-23   5-26-2-11   23-14-14-24-2

___ ___ ___ ___ ___ ___   ___ ___ ___ ___   ___ ___ ___ ___

2-21-16-22-20-11-25-16-14   18-14-18-15-16-19

___ ___ ___ ___ ___ ___ ___ ___ ___   ___ ___ ___ ___ ___ ___

9-14-16-2-14-2   26-13-12   16-14-21-22-11-14

___ ___ ___ ___ ___ ___   ___ ___ ___   ___ ___ ___ ___ ___ ___

11-10-14-18   11-15   19-15-25-16   20-26-16-14-13-11.

___ ___ ___ ___   ___ ___   ___ ___ ___ ___   ___ ___ ___ ___ ___ ___.

Then, begin to memorize this week's verses.

15

Week 2: One body
Day 2: My part in the body

As Jim and Janet walked away from Pastor Beall's office, Jim said: "I don't think I have ever thought of *church* as a *body*, Janet. I have thought of the word as a *building*—a place where we go to study the Bible, to train for service, and to hear Pastor Beall preach."

"Me, too, Jim," said Janet thoughtfully. "Now I understand that the church is a body. Each member is like a part of the body that helps the other parts of the body by doing its special work. If I didn't have *feet*, I could not walk. Yet my feet cannot do the work of my hands. Each one has a special work to do."

Jim smiled. "Right—and I learned the hard way that I can't *walk* with my *hands.* Do you remember when I tried and skinned my face when I fell?"

Jim and Janet climbed on their bicycles, still talking. "The members of our church are not only like a body; they are also like a big family, aren't they?" said Janet. "Mother can't *teach* like Mr. Robinson, and *he* can't care for sick people like Mother does. Yet both have a special work to do in our church."

"Right," said Jim. "Remember when Mrs. Isaacs had her operation, and Mother stayed with her at the hospital all night? I see that *every* member of the church has a special work to do for the others. It's like our family; each family member has his own chores to do."

Janet asked: "What about *us*, Jim? *We* are now members of the body of Christ, just like the others. So is Richard. Do we have to wait until we are grown up to serve the Lord Jesus? Do only older people serve him?"

HOW DOES THE BIBLE ANSWER JANET'S QUESTION? READ ROMANS 12:5.
Which statement below says the same thing as these verses? (Underline your answer)
1. All church members do the same things.
2. Christians do not have to help one another.
3. We are like a human body. We do not all serve the Lord in the same way, but we all can help one another.

THE ACTIONS DESCRIBED IN ROMANS 12:6-9 ARE REWRITTEN HERE TO EXPLAIN HOW RICHARD, JIM, JANET, *AND YOU* CAN SERVE OTHERS. CIRCLE THE ONES *YOU* ARE ABLE TO DO AT THIS TIME.

PROPHECY: Preaching a sermon, like Pastor Beall does

SERVICE: Helping to clean up after a Sunday School party

TEACHING: Explaining the Bible, like Mr. Robinson does

EXHORTING: Encouraging someone who is unhappy or discour-
aged

GIVING: Using some of my allowance or money to support the
work of my church

LEADING: Helping a boy like Richard follow Jesus more closely

SHOWING MERCY: Forgetting someone's bad points

LOVING: Caring deeply for someone

HOW MANY OF THESE EIGHT THINGS CAN YOU DO?
In the puzzle, you will discover what Jim and Janet decided they
can do. All the words for this puzzle are in the list of the eight
actions or their definitions.

Clues

Across	Down:
3. What Pastor Beall does	1. Cleaning up
5. Supporting the work of the church	2. Caring for someone
6. Helping others follow Jesus	4. Encouraging someone
8. Forgetting bad points (2 words)	7. Explaining the Bible

Answers: 1. serving; 2. loving; 3. preaching; 4. exhorting; 5. giving;
6. leading; 7. teaching; 8. showing mercy.

SECRET CODE MESSAGE:
1-26-13-14-11   12-15-14-2   3-15-25-16;   1-22-18

——— ——— ——— ———   ——— ——— ——— ———   ——— ——— ——— ———   ——— ——— ———

12-15-14-2   2-22-7.

——— ——— ——— ———   ——— ——— ———.

HAVE YOU MEMORIZED THE BIBLE VERSES FOR THIS
WEEK?

Week 2: One body
Day 3: The gift of serving

Before you read about Jim and Janet, *write 1 Corinthians 12:18 from memory.*

_____

_____

_____

_____

Can you *from memory* fill in these blanks?

We are _____ _____ in union with _____, and we are all _____ to each other as different _____ of one _____ (Romans 12:5).

It was Saturday afternoon, and Jim had gone over to see Richard. Mr. Robinson had encouraged Jim to visit him, explaining that Richard needed help with his devotional time. Because his parents were not yet Christians, Richard did not get much help from them in preparing for Sunday School each week.

"Hi, Jim," said Richard as he opened the door. "Come in. I've been trying to study my Sunday School lesson for tomorrow, but I don't understand about the special gifts God gives us when we become Christians."

Jim replied: "The verse in 1 Corinthians 12:7 has helped me. It says: 'The Spirit's presence is shown in some way in each person for the good of all.' A *spiritual gift* is a special strength God's Spirit gives us to help others. Look at it this way, Richard: when we play baseball, you are the best pitcher. I am the best batter. Pedro is the best first baseman we have. God made each of us so that we could play baseball, but he made us with different *abilities* to use when we play. Becoming a Christian is receiving a new life. When this new life is given to us, we are given spiritual abilities to use as we work beside other Christians."

"Oh, I see," said Richard. "Mr. Robinson told me I should begin to use the *gift of serving.* He explained the word actually is talking about people who serve others at mealtime. Did he mean I am supposed to help serve at the church banquet next week?"

"Perhaps," said Jim, laughing. "But there are other ways *we* can use God's power in us to serve others."

HERE'S A SECRET MESSAGE FROM RICHARD AND JIM TO YOU:

25-13-12-14-16-5-22-13-14   11-10-14   23-26-19-2

_ _ _ _ _ _ _ _ _   _ _ _   _ _ _ _

19-15-25   21-26-13   25-2-14   19-15-25-16

_ _ _   _ _ _   _ _ _   _ _ _ _

17-22-3-11   15-3   2-14-16-9-22-13-17:

_ _ _ _   _ _   _ _ _ _ _ _ _:

Record the pastor's message on my cassette recorder and play it for a church member who is sick.

Pull weeds in the church yard.

Help with refreshments during Vacation Bible School.

Help straighten up the church library when it closes.

Put away recreation equipment.

Help clean a house for a church member who is ill.

Baby-sit free for a couple who want to attend a Bible study.

Make cookies for a Sunday School party.

Collect the music after choir rehearsal.

Write a letter to a boy or girl who was in my Sunday School department who has moved to another town.

WHAT ELSE COULD YOU DO?

Week 2: One body
Day 4: The gift of giving

CHECK UP ON YOURSELF:

I can repeat these verses from memory:

WRITE REFERENCE OF VERSE HERE:	PLACE *X* IN BOX IF YOU CAN QUOTE THE VERSE FROM MEMORY	
PSALM _____	☐	LAST
2 CORINTHIANS		WEEK
_____	☐	
1 CORINTHIANS		THIS
_____	☐	WEEK
ROMANS _____	☐	

"Hurry," said Father. "We are going to be late for the missionary service if we do not leave at once." Jim quickly ran to the desk and grabbed his Bible. Along with it, he snatched his billfold and pushed it deep into his pocket.

As they rode to church in the car, Jim and Janet compared the amounts of money each had earned during the past week. Janet had two dollar bills, earned by baby-sitting. Jim had polished all of Dad's shoes and had seven quarters in his billfold.

The missionary who spoke at the church service was from Thailand. He told of the many poor refugees who had fled from the Communists. He showed slides of people who were living in tents. Janet whispered to Jim in the darkness, "Look, Jim, those children are our age!"

When the missionary finished speaking, a special offering for foreign missions was taken. Pastor Beall explained that the money received would be divided among all the missionary work around the world. He said: "I have been teaching you about spiritual gifts. Along with the gift of *serving*, God has also given us the gift of *giving*. When God tells us to give our possessions for his work, he promises to replace our supply. Join me in giving. Give what God tells you to give to this missionary offering."

Pastor Beall looked over the audience and saw Jim. "Jim, I see you have brought your Bible to the service. Will you find 2 Corinthians 9:11 and read it for us?"

Jim's heart thumped as he quickly found the verse. He read aloud: "He will always make you rich enough to be generous at all times, so that many will thank God for your gifts which they receive from us."

When the offering plate passed by, Jim placed four of his quarters in it. Janet put one of her dollar bills in it. In the car on the way home, Janet whispered to Jim: "I was proud of you, Jim! You read that verse very well."

Jim answered: "Janet, God has given us so much. I'm glad we gave to the missionary offering. The gift of giving is important for us to use. I will pray that our money will help the people we saw in the slides tonight and all the others around the world."

SEE A WORD

"SEE A WORD" PUZZLE

```
V G N I T S A C D A O R B X R A Q C F
R M J K E T G C L N B D S L O O H C S
C U L P A S T O R S E F N Y R K T H D
F S B R C J D L Q Y Z R B T M L J U Q
H I T Z H B F L B E S E E G U F E R N
K C Y S E M I E F Z J C J Q X Y G C K
G I C L R D L G X D C M B G Z K D H S
M A K A S B M E Y J C E W R D L X E E
D N R T S T S I T N E D O C T O R S L
Q S L I E V A N G E L I S T S K O O B
L M C P D K N J Q Z X C B B K L G M I
T Z R S J X K F T D W I M T C F C T B
J G F O O D C N R T Z N X G B M E J N
M L U H R G R Q X W S E M I N A R Y Z
```

In this puzzle are 17 words telling how our gifts to Jesus are used by missionaries. Try to locate these words. Some go across, some go up or down, and some are backward. Circle the words you find.

Answers: broadcasting, musicians, teachers, college, churches, Bibles, medicine, hospitals, pastors, schools, refugees, dentists, doctors, evangelists, books, food, and seminary.

Week 2: One body
Day 5: Review

COMPLETE THIS PAGE BY YOURSELF. THEN SHOW
IT TO YOUR PARENTS. YOU MAY HAVE A SPECIAL
FRIEND WHO GAVE THIS SURVIVAL KIT TO YOU. IF
SO, ALSO SHOW IT TO THAT PERSON.

MY DEVOTIONAL TIME

Do you have a devotional time each day? Ten devotional guides
have been provided, including today, in this SURVIVAL KIT. *Circle
the number of days you have used it in your devotional times:*

1 2 3 4 5 6 7 8 9 10

MY SCRIPTURE MEMORY

Try to write from memory the four verses you have memorized:
PSALM 119:11

2 CORINTHIANS 5:17

1 CORINTHIANS 12:18

ROMANS 12:5

FILL IN THE BLANKS ON THE PALM AND THUMB OF THE HAND DIAGRAM. (If you need help, look back at pages 14-15.)

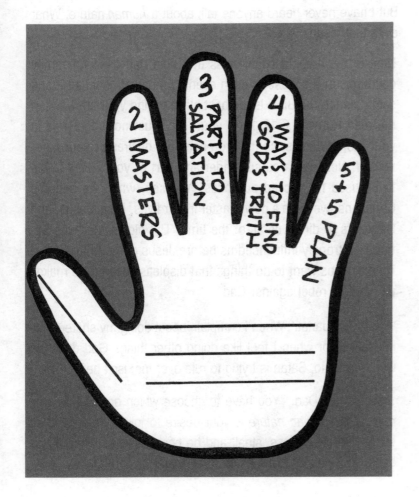

DRAW A PICTURE IN THE BOX BELOW THAT EXPLAINS THAT THE *CHURCH* IS A *BODY:*

TWO GIFTS GOD GIVES US FOR USE AS CHRISTIANS ARE:

THE GIFT OF S _ _ _ _ _ _.

THE GIFT OF G _ _ _ _ _.

ASK ONE OF YOUR PARENTS TO SIGN BELOW AFTER YOU HAVE SHOWN THEM TODAY'S REVIEW:

I have reviewed the work my child has done in the Survival Kit.

SIGNED_____

Week 3: Two masters
Day 1: Jesus has come! Satan is unhappy!

READ GALATIANS 5:16-17 BEFORE READING THESE WORDS.

"Dad, please help me with a question I had during my devotional time today," said Janet.

Dad looked up from his breakfast: "Sure, Lollipop!" (Dad had called Janet by that special name as long as she could remember.) "What's the question?"

"Galatians 5:16 tells us to let the Spirit direct our lives."

Jim spoke up quickly: "*I* know what *that* means, Janet. That's talking about letting the spirit of Jesus, who now lives in us, guide us."

Dad smiled. Jim often tried to be a *big brother* to Janet, even though they were twins. "Right you are, Jim."

Janet continued: "Well, I understand *that* part, too, Jim. But the Scripture says, 'You will not satisfy the desires of the human nature.' We study about *nature* in school: birds, plants, and animals. But I have never heard anyone talk about a *human* nature. What does that mean, Dad?"

Next to the breakfast table was the Bible Dad used for family devotions at the close of each evening meal. He opened it and said: "Janet, the Bible is the best place to find your answer. Let me read Romans 6:12-13 to you. 'Sin must no longer rule in your mortal bodies, so that you obey the desires of your natural self. Nor must you surrender any part of yourselves to sin to be used for wicked purposes.' You see, when we become Christians, we have a new Master in our lives. He is Jesus, and He wants to direct us all of the time. The old master was Satan. He strongly influenced us before Jesus came to live in us. He makes us want to do things that displease Jesus. He makes us want to rebel against God."

"Yes," said Janet. "When I complain about doing my share of the housework or when I feel like doing other things God does not want me to do, Satan is trying to rule over me, isn't he?"

"Right," said Dad. "You have to choose which one will be your ruler. Your *human nature* is your desire to follow Satan and do things like cheat, fuss, steal, and be bossy. We do these things because Satan encourages us to do them."

A SECRET MESSAGE FROM JIM AND JANET:

23-16-22-11-14   22-13   21-15-12-14   11-10-14

_ _ _ _ _ _ _ _ _ _ _ _ _ _

11-10-22-13-17   2-26-11-26-13

_ _ _ _ _ _ _ _ _ _

14-13-21-15-25-16-26-17-14-2   19-15-25   11-15

_ _ _ _ _ _ _ _ _ _ _ _ _ _ _

12-15:

_ _:

MY SECRET ANSWER, IN CODE:

_____

_____

_____

Add this to your prayer list on page 11.
Ask Jesus to take charge in this area of your life!

LEARN YOUR VERSES AS THOUGH YOUR SPIRITUAL GROWTH DEPENDED ON IT... BECAUSE IT DOES!

MEMORY VERSE

Week 3: Two masters
Day 2: Rejecting Satan

Janet, Richard, and Jim were helping to decorate the fellowship hall of the church building. Mr. Robinson and other teachers were preparing the tables. Janet, Richard, and Jim were assigned the job of blowing up 100 balloons, to be attached to the ceiling by strings.

Mr. Robinson had watched them huff and puff. Smiling, he tied a string around the neck of a yellow balloon Richard had just blown up. He said: "I will use this balloon to teach you a lesson about Satan. Richard, hold it up to the light." As Richard did so, Mr. Robinson said: "Do you see the places where the rubber is thin, and the color becomes lighter? Janet, if Richard had blown just *one more breath of air* into it, one of those weak spots would have been unable to resist the air pressure within. You see, when a balloon explodes, it is always the *weakest point* that breaks."

"What does that teach about Satan?" asked Jim.

Mr. Robinson replied: "Satan knows the weakest place in each of our lives. He knows how to put pressure on us in that area. He always tries to control us in that part of our life. For example, if

Satan knows we are selfish, he will try to make us think it is all right to refuse to help our brother or sister when they really need us. He uses our weakness to control us."

Janet said: "Mr. Robinson, the first murder in the Bible happened when Cain killed his own brother Abel. Satan knew Cain was *jealous* of his brother. That was his weak point, wasn't it? His jealousy caused him to murder."

Jim was quiet for a moment and then said, "Mr. Robinson, if Satan knows our weak spots, it's a pretty important thing for *us* to know them, too, isn't it?"

"Yes, Jim," said Mr. Robinson. "It may be jealousy, or selfishness, or hatred of someone else. I think each one of us truly knows the place where we are weak and where Satan might try to gain control."

Richard spoke up: "Our weaknesses are like the thin places in the balloon, aren't they? Satan knows every one of them!"

A SECRET MESSAGE FROM JIM, JANET, AND RICHARD TO YOU:

23-14   21-10-15-15-2-14

—— ——————

23-10-15   16-25-5-14-2   25-2.   19-15-25

——— —————— ——. ———

8-14-5-15-13-17   11-15   19-15-25-16

—————— —— ————

21-10-15-22-21-14.

—————— —.

According to Galatians 5:22-23, what will be the results of Jesus' ruling over us?
UNSCRAMBLE THESE WORDS, ALL FOUND IN THIS SCRIPTURE PASSAGE. WHEN YOU DO, YOU WILL DISCOVER A WORD TELLING WHAT JESUS GIVES US OVER OUR WEAKNESSES.

ATFLESFIHUNS

EVOL

ECNEITAP

APECE

IMUHYTIL

NDOSOSEG

LESF-NOCLOTR

YJO

DNNSIKES

Week 3: Two masters
Day 3: Choosing your master

Janet and her best friend, Susan, were spending the night at Susan's house. Dad had said to Janet: "Lollipop, if you and Susan don't get any more sleep *tonight* than you did when she spent the night at *our* house, you both will be too sleepy to go to the zoo with us tomorrow!" Laughingly, Janet promised him they would not speak a single word to each other after midnight.

It was just about midnight, however, when Susan said: "Janet, since I accepted Jesus as my Master, I have been ashamed of something that I do. The boy who sits in front of me at school is a good student. He doesn't hide his answers when we take tests. Sometimes, when I am not sure of the answer, I will look over his shoulder when he holds up his paper to read it. Several times I have changed my answer to the one he has written down. I have asked Jesus to forgive me, but then I do it again! What can I do to stop this bad habit?"

Janet reached into her small suitcase and found her Bible. "Susan, I have read a Scripture passage in my devotional time that helps answer your question." Opening to Romans 7:19-20, Janet read

aloud: "I don't do the good I want to do; instead, I do the evil that I do not want to do. If I do what I don't want to do, this means that I am no longer the one who does it; instead, it is the sin that lives in me."

"Wow! That sure sounds like *me*, doesn't it" Susan said. "I do things I really do not want to do when I steal answers from someone else's test paper."

Janet replied: "Mother explained to me that Satan will always try to encourage us to do what displeases God. He will touch us at our weak point. I guess we *all* have a weakness when it comes to making good grades on tests, don't we, Susan?"

Susan had been looking at the verse Janet had read. Suddenly, she brightened up and said: "Janet! Here's *another* verse that helps. Listen to Romans 8:5: 'Those who live as their human nature tells them to, have their minds controlled by what human nature wants. Those who live as the Spirit tells them to, have their minds controlled by what the Spirit wants.' "

WHAT DOES THAT VERSE MEAN?
Using words from the verse just quoted by Susan, complete these sentences to show the contrast:

IF I LIVE THE WAY MY H__ __ __ __ N __ __ __ __ __ TELLS ME

TO LIVE, THEN MY MIND WILL BE CONTROLLED BY WHAT

H _ _ _ _ N _ _ _ _ _ WANTS.

IF I LIVE THE WAY THE S_ _ _ _ _ OF JESUS TELLS ME

TO LIVE, THEN MY MIND WILL BE CONTROLLED BY WHAT

THE S_ _ _ _ _ OF JESUS WANTS.

Susan answered: "Janet, it's almost like I have a little switch inside me. If I turn that switch to allow the Spirit of Jesus to direct my life, I know I will resist the desire to cheat. My problem is caused by *not* switching the control of my mind to Jesus, isn't it?"

"Yes," said Janet. "We *all* have to decide that we will let the Spirit of Jesus tell us how to live. When Jesus is master, Satan cannot be master. *We only have one master at a time controlling us. We choose who will be master.*"

A SECRET MESSAGE FROM JIM AND JANET:

23-14   10-26-9-14   26-5-16-14-26-12-19

_ _   _ _ _ _   _ _ _ _ _ _

18-14-18-15-16-22-4-14-12   15-25-16

_ _ _ _ _ _ _ _ _   _ _ _.

9-14-16-2-14-2   3-15-16   11-10-22-2   23-14-14-24.

_ _ _ _ _ _   _ _ _   _ _ _ _   _ _ _ _.

WHO IS MASTER IN EACH OF THESE SITUATIONS?

JESUS SATAN

☐   ☐   1. You ask to borrow a pencil from the boy at the desk in front of you, but you don't plan to give it back.

☐   ☐   2. You are watching a TV program. Mother asks you to help her clean the house. You decide Mother's desires are more important than the TV program; you go to help her.

☐   ☐   3. You notice no one is watching you in a grocery store. You take a candy bar and hide it in your pocket. Later, you eat it.

☐   ☐   4. You are riding your bike home from school, going much too fast. The school guard asks you to slow down. You apologize for speeding and slow down at once.

☐   ☐   5. You are in the lunch line, and a boy steps in front of you, breaking into the line. You knock his books out of his hand, shouting at him to get to the back of the line.

1, 3 and 5 are examples of Satan's ruling.

Week 3: Two masters
Day 4: Jesus, my Master forever!

During his devotional time Jim had already studied about the gift of serving. He now put into practice what he had learned. He and Dad spent each Saturday afternoon working in Mr. Johnston's yard. Mr. Johnston, an elderly deacon in the church, had been ill for several weeks. As he sat on the porch, Jim and Dad mowed his lawn and watered his flowerbeds.

One afternoon after the work was finished, Jim drank a cold glass of lemonade and visited with Mr. Johnston. The wise old man said: "Jim, one day you will be a fine Christian man like your father. You have already started to let Jesus be master in your life. Now, Son, let me tell you something about myself.

"I accepted Jesus when I was your age. I remember it as though it were yesterday. But when I became a teenager, I discovered that while Jesus continued to be my *Savior*, I had failed to invite him to continue to be my master. So I had to let him be master. You see, Jim, when I was *your* age I could not give him my life as a *16-year old* boy. I had to wait until I became 16 to do it! And then, Jim, I had to give him control of my life again when I went to college. As a boy of *16*, I could not promise him the life of a boy of *19*. And so it has been throughout my life. I have learned that I must wait for each day to come before I can let Jesus be master for me on that day."

Jim thought about Mr. Johnston's words. Then he said: "I think I know what you mean. If I want Jesus to be my master *forever*, I must choose him to be my Master *each day*. Is that right?"

"Yes, Jim. Just because he is forever and ever your *Savior* does not mean he will automatically be your *Master* each day. You must daily give him the right to do that."

"Mr. Johnston, I have a friend named Richard. He became a Christian about the same time I did. Lately, Richard has been skipping Sunday School and going to the store near the church to buy candy. I guess he does not know how important it is to give Jesus the throne *every day*."

WOULD YOU HELP RICHARD UNDERSTAND WHAT MR. JOHNSTON SAID?
Which of these Bible verses would you ask him to read? Look up each verse. Then, put an *X* in the box next to each verse you would show Richard:
☐ GALATIANS 5:25   ☐ 1 JOHN 2:28
☐ EPHESIANS 4:24   ☐ ROMANS 6:16

ANSWER: ALL OF THESE VERSES WOULD HELP RICHARD.

SECRET MESSAGE FROM JIM AND JANET:

11-15-18-15-16-16-15-23   19-15-25   23-22-5-5

_ _ _ _ _ _ _ _   _ _ _   _ _ _ _

2-10-26-16-14   26-5-5   2-22-7

_ _ _ _ _   _ _ _   _ _ _

18-14-18-15-16-19   9-14-16-2-14-2   23-22-11-10

_ _ _ _ _ _   _ _ _ _ _ _   _ _ _ _

19-15-25-16   20-26-16-14-13-11.

_ _ _ _   _ _ _ _ _ _—.

Week 3: Two masters
Day 5: Review

COMPLETE THIS PAGE BY YOURSELF. THEN SHOW IT TO YOUR PARENTS. YOU MAY HAVE A SPECIAL FRIEND WHO GAVE THIS SURVIVAL KIT TO YOU. IF SO, ALSO SHOW IT TO THAT PERSON.

How is your daily devotional time developing?
Fifteen days of material have been provided in your SURVIVAL KIT, including today.

Circle the number of days you have had a devotional time:

1   2   3   4   5   6   7   8   9   10   11   12   13   14   15

MY SCRIPTURE MEMORY

I can repeat the following verses from memory (be prepared to do so, if asked to quote any one of them by your parent):

☐ PSALM 119:11
☐ ROMANS 6:14
☐ ROMANS 12:5
☐ 1 CORINTHIANS 12:18
☐ 2 CORINTHIANS 5:17
☐ GALATIANS 5:22-23

FILL IN THE BLANKS ON THE PALM, THUMB, AND FINGER OF THE HAND DIAGRAM:

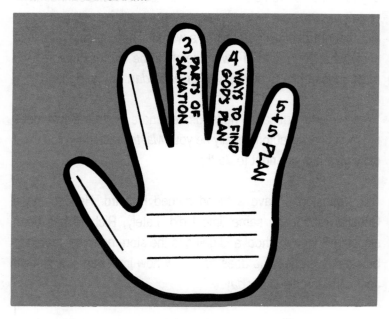

CLUES

Across

2. Human n__ __ __ __ __ (See Day 1.)
3. What is the name of one of the two masters? S__ __ __ __ __.
5. When Satan attacks, he does so through our w__ __ __ sp__ __ __. (2 words) (See Day 2.)
7. A fruit of the Spirit is h__ __ __ __ __ __ __.
8. Who chooses who will be master in my life? __ __.

CHECK UP CARD (Put in your Bible)

BIBLE VERSES	MEMORIZED	SHARED WITH PARENT	SHARED WITH FRIEND

MY SECRET CODE CARD

1	2	3	4	5	6	7	8	9	10	11	12	13
J	S	F	Z	L	Q	X	B	V	H	T	D	N

14	15	16	17	18	19	20	21	22	23	24	25	26
E	O	R	G	M	Y	P	C	I	W	K	U	A

MY SECRET CODE CARD

1	2	3	4	5	6	7	8	9	10	11	12	13
J	S	F	Z	L	Q	X	B	V	H	T	D	N

14	15	16	17	18	19	20	21	22	23	24	25	26
E	O	R	G	M	Y	P	C	I	W	K	U	A

Use your SECRET CODE CARD to decode messages from Jim and Janet.

Use your SECRET CODE CARD to decode messages from Jim and Janet.

INSTRUCTIONS FOR MEMORIZING BIBLE VERSES

1. Use scissors to cut out the cards.
2. Use the side of the card that gives the Bible verse. Memorize two verses a week.
3. A good plan is to carry the cards in your pocket. Use your spare time to memorize them. Memorize verses as you walk to school, wait for meals, or while commercials are on TV.
4. Review each verse already learned by using the side of each memory verse card which gives only the reference.
5. Repeat the reference *before* and *after* you say the verse. Then you'll remember where to find it in your Bible.
6. Recite your memory verses to your parents once a week when you show them your Review Pages.
7. Choose a "Special Friend." Share your verses with this friend once a week.
8. Also, give your "Special Friend" a SECRET CODE CARD. You can then send secret messages to each other.

WEEK 6 Verse 2
5 & 5 PLAN
Romans 1:16 (GNB)

WEEK 5 Verse 2
4 WAYS TO FIND GOD'S TRUTH
2 Peter 1:21 (GNB)

WEEK 4 Verse 2
3 PARTS TO SALVATION
1 Corinthians 10:13 (GNB)

WEEK 3 Verse 2
2 MASTERS
Galatians 5:22-23 (GNB)

WEEK 2 Verse 2
1 BODY
Romans 12:5 (GNB)

WEEK 1 Verse 2
MY NEW LIFE
2 Corinthians 5:17 (GNB)

WEEK 6 Verse 1
5 & 5 PLAN
Matthew 7:7-8 (GNB)

WEEK 5 Verse 1
4 WAYS TO FIND GOD'S TRUTH
1 Corinthians 2:14 (GNB)

WEEK 4 Verse 1
3 PARTS TO SALVATION
Philippians 1:6 (GNB)

WEEK 3 Verse 1
2 MASTERS
Romans 6:14 (GNB)

WEEK 2 Verse 1
1 BODY
1 Corinthians 12:18 (GNB)

WEEK 1 Verse 1
MY NEW LIFE
Psalm 119:11 (GNB)

WEEK 6 Verse 2
5 & 5 PLAN
I have complete confidence in the gospel; it is God's power to save all who believe.

Romans 1:16 (GNB)

WEEK 5 Verse 2
4 WAYS TO FIND GOD'S TRUTH
No prophetic message ever came just from the will of man, but men were under the control of the Holy Spirit as they spoke the message that came from God.

2 Peter 1:21 (GNB)

WEEK 4 Verse 2
3 PARTS TO SALVATION
God . . . will not allow you to be tested beyond your power to remain firm; at the time you are put to the test, he will give you the strength to endure it, and so provide you with a way out.

1 Corinthians 10:13 (GNB)

WEEK 3 Verse 2
2 MASTERS
The Spirit produces love, joy, peace, patience, kindness, goodness, faithfulness, humility, and self-control.

Galatians 5:22-23 (GNB)

WEEK 2 Verse 2
1 BODY
We are one body in union with Christ, and we are all joined to each other as different parts of one body.

Romans 12:5 (GNB)

WEEK 1 Verse 2
MY NEW LIFE
When anyone is joined to Christ, he is a new being; the old is gone, the new has come.

2 Corinthians 5:17 (GNB)

WEEK 6 Verse 1
5 & 5 PLAN
Ask, and you will receive; seek, and you will find; knock, and the door will be opened to you. For everyone who asks will receive, and anyone who seeks will find, and the door will be opened to him who knocks.

Matthew 7:7-8 (GNB)

WEEK 5 Verse 1
4 WAYS TO FIND GOD'S TRUTH
Whoever does not have the Spirit cannot receive the gifts that come from God's Spirit. Such a person really does not understand them.

1 Corinthians 2:14 (GNB)

WEEK 4 Verse 1
3 PARTS TO SALVATION
I am sure that God, who began this good work in you, will carry it on until it is finished on the Day of Christ Jesus.

Philippians 1:6 (GNB)

WEEK 3 Verse 1
2 MASTERS
Sin must not be your master; for you do not live under law but under God's grace.

Romans 6:14 (GNB)

WEEK 2 Verse 1
1 BODY
God put every different part in the body just as he wanted it to be.

1 Corinthians 12:18 (GNB)

WEEK 1 Verse 1
MY NEW LIFE
I keep your law in my heart, so that I will not sin against you.

Psalm 119:11 (GNB)

Down

1. What is the name of the other master? J__ __ __ __.
4. How often must I give Jesus the throne of my life? EACH __ __ __. (See Day 5.)
6. Another fruit of the Spirit is p__ __ __ __ __ __ __.

COMPLETE THIS PUZZLE, USING CLUES PROVIDED:

The answer to puzzle is on page 45.

Write a description of what can happen when Jesus or Satan controls your life. Show it to your parents.

JESUS IN CONTROL:_____

_____

_____

_____

_____

SATAN IN CONTROL:_____

_____

_____

_____

_____

ASK ONE OF YOUR PARENTS TO SIGN BELOW AFTER YOU HAVE SHOWN THEM TODAY'S REVIEW:

I have reviewed the work my child has done in the Survival Kit.
SIGNED:_____

Week 4: Three parts to salvation
Day 1: Salvation past, present, and future

Jim and Richard met on the lawn of the church before Sunday School time. Jim had given him this secret message on Thursday:

26-2-24   19-15-25-16   18-15-11-10-14-16   22-3

___ _____ _____ __

19-15-25   18-26-19   14-26-11   26-11   18-19

___ ___ ___ __ __

10-15-25-2-14   2-25-13-12-26-19   26-3-11-14-16

____ _____ _____

21-10-25-16-21-10.

_____.

Richard said, "I'm looking forward to going home from church with you today, Jim!" Together, they walked to their Sunday School department.

Mr. Robinson greeted them: "Richard, I'm glad to have you back with us! I missed you last Sunday."

Richard looked guilty, and said: "Well, Mr. Robinson, I am sorry I missed last week. I will be coming *every* week from now on, I hope!" Jim noticed that Richard did not seem sure he would *keep* that promise.

Mr. Robinson asked George to read Philippians 1:6 aloud. George was the fastest boy in the group when it came to finding Bible verses! In a flash, he found the verse and began to read: "And so I am sure that God, who began this good work in you, will carry it on until it is finished on the Day of Christ Jesus."

Mr. Robinson had prepared this diagram on the chalkboard:

THE BEGINNING POINT	SALVATION DAY BY DAY	THE FINAL EVENT
God began this good work in you...	God will carry it on...	Until it is finished on the day of Christ Jesus.

"Jim, what does the part of the diagram mean which says, 'THE BEGINNING POINT'?" asked Mr. Robinson.

Jim replied, "Well, it means that salvation started in my life when I accepted Jesus as my Lord and Savior."

"Right, Jim," said Mr. Robinson. "Now, George, what does the part of the diagram mean which says, 'THE FINAL EVENT'?"

George said: "One day Jesus is going to return. When he comes back, it means our salvation will be *finished.* But I don't understand that, Mr. Robinson. Does that mean I will no longer *have* my salvation when Jesus comes back?"

Richard's hand shot up into the air. "I can help George, Mr. Robinson! It means we are going to be set free from Satan forever when Jesus returns, doesn't it?"

"Right," said Mr. Robinson. "Salvation is in three parts. At the beginning, we are freed from the penalty of sin. When we ask Jesus to live in us, he takes away forever the judgment for our wrong actions. Then, in the future, when he returns, we are going to have the presence of Satan removed from our lives."

Richard said: "What about the other part—SALVATION DAY BY DAY? I think that's *my* biggest need."

Mr. Robinson replied: "That means Jesus has come to give Christians power over Satan each day we live. Notice, Richard, that God gives us this daily freedom from sin's power. We'll learn more about that next Sunday. I hope you will be here."

"Oh, I wouldn't miss being here for *anything,*" said Richard.

"Good," said Mr. Robinson. "Remember, there are three parts to our salvation. In the PAST, we were set free from the PENALTY of sin; in the PRESENT, we are freed from the POWER OF SIN; and in the FUTURE, the PRESENCE OF SIN."

Week 4: Three parts to salvation
Day 2: Salvation day by day

BEFORE YOU BEGIN TO READ TODAY'S STORY, SPEND A
LITTLE TIME MEMORIZING 1 CORINTHIANS 10:13. IT WILL
HELP YOU UNDERSTAND THE SUNDAY SCHOOL LESSON
MR. ROBINSON TEACHES IN THE STORY TODAY AND
TOMORROW!

Richard and Jim came to their Sunday School department ten
minutes early the next Sunday morning. Both were eager to hear
what their teacher would say about SALVATION DAY BY DAY. As
they entered the room, they saw Mr. Robinson setting up a small
stepladder in the middle of the room. Surprised, Jim asked, "What
are we going to do with *that* during Sunday School, Mr.
Robinson?"

Smiling, Mr. Robinson said: "You'll find out when we begin, Jim. In
the meantime, would you and Richard review your Scripture memory verse, 1 Corinthians 10:13? I'll be with you in a few minutes."
With that Mr. Robinson left the room.

Still not understanding why the stepladder had been set up, the
two boys began helping each other recite their memory verse.

Soon others arrived, and Mr. Robinson returned with a towel in his
hand.

"Do you trust me to keep my word?" he asked.

"Sure," the group said quickly.

"Well, then, I would like to ask one of you to climb up this stepladder and stand on the top step. I promise you that I will not let you fall."

The group laughed. It seemed like such a simple thing to climb up the stepladder and stand on the top of it. Richard jumped up and quickly climbed the stepladder. He stood triumphantly on the top of it, his hands on his hips.

"Thank you, Richard," said the teacher. "Now I want to ask you to stand in that position for the next fifteen minutes while I teach the lesson. Oh, I almost forgot. I want to ask you to let me tie this towel over your eyes."

Richard, not looking as happy now, did not want the other boys to think he was a coward. He let himself be blindfolded. During the next few minutes, he heard Mr. Robinson teaching the lesson, but he began to feel as though he were standing at the top of a high building. The step beneath his feet began to feel smaller and smaller. He did not move about much, fearing he would lose his balance and fall. He began counting the time under his breath. Each minute seemed like an hour.

After many minutes had passed, Richard decided to turn around and face the opposite direction. By now, his feet and legs had become stiff. As he moved, the blindfold made it even harder for him to keep his balance. He felt himself falling! The stepladder began to sway beneath him, and he knew he was about to fall. Suddenly, Mr. Robinson's strong hands were about his waist.

"Richard, I promised you that if you would stand up there for fifteen minutes, I would not let you fall. I am keeping my word." Carefully, Mr. Robinson helped him regain his balance.

Then he said, still holding Richard's arm, "Tell me, Richard, did you *expect* me to be there at the moment you began to fall?"

"No, not really," said Richard. "I thought I was all by myself and that if I fell, no one would help me in time."

Mr. Robinson removed the blindfold, saying, "But Richard, I was standing beside you the *entire time*, with my eyes on you as I taught the group."

"That's right, Richard," said Jim. "He never took his eyes off you for a second."

"Do you understand what our memory verse promises us? *'At the time you are put to the test, he will give you the strength to endure it, and so provide you with a way out.'* Each day we live, he is caring for us."

Week 4: Three parts to salvation
Day 3: Jesus keeps us each day we live!

As Richard climbed down from the stepladder, the group was quiet. Each one was thinking of the lesson Mr. Robinson had taught them. "I knew you would not let Richard fall," said Jim.

"Well, Jim," said Mr. Robinson, "do you believe that our Lord Jesus Christ is going to keep *his* word? If so, then his salvation is not only for *yesterday* and *tomorrow*, but he will save us *today*. Each time we think we are not able to live with Jesus on the throne, we must remember that in that very *moment*, he is reaching out to support us."

Jim said: "Yesterday when we were having breakfast, Dad told us the Bible calls the Holy Spirit the 'One Called to Walk Beside Us and Help.' I guess God really cares about what happens to us each day, if he walks beside us just to hold on to us when we need help."

Richard slowly said to the group: "I guess you have noticed that I have been missing Sunday School recently. I *plan* to come, but then I decide to stop at the store where they have pinball machines, and I begin to play the games. Next, I decide to use my Sunday School offering to play another game or two. When I have spent all my money, I really get mad at myself. I have spent my money during the Sunday School hour, and then I go home. I guess the reason the Lord had *me* climb that stepladder instead of one of *you* was to teach me today's lesson in a special way."

Mr. Robinson spoke softly as he said: "Richard, you are a fine boy. It took courage to share that with us. You are right. Jesus *is* standing beside you when you pass by the store with the pinball machines. He *will* help you make the right decision. All you have to do is stop and talk to him about it. Say: 'Lord, I know I want to go in there and play. You have promised that you would not allow me to be tempted beyond my power to resist. I thank you for giving me victory right now over my desire.' Son, I know from my *own* life that in that moment he will give you strength, and your desire to do the wrong thing will stop."

Before the Sunday School hour ended, each boy thanked the Lord Jesus for SALVATION DAY BY DAY and prayed particularly for Richard and his special problem. Jim told Janet it was one of the *best* Sunday School lessons he had ever heard!

A SECRET MESSAGE FROM RICHARD AND JIM TO YOU:

10-26-9-14   19-15-25   26   3-16-22-14-13-12

____ ___ _ _____

23-10-15   13-14-14-12-2   11-15   24-13-15-23

___ _____ __ ____

23-10-26-11   19-15-25   10-26-9-14

____ ___ ____

5-14-26-16-13-14-12?   2-10-26-16-14   22-11

_____?   _____ __

13-15-23!

___

WHY NOT ADD TO YOUR PRAYER LIST (PAGE 11) THOSE
SPECIAL TIMES WHEN YOU ARE TEMPTED? ASK THE LORD
TO STRENGTHEN YOU IN A SPECIAL WAY WHEN YOU FACE
THEM.

Week 4: Three parts to salvation
Day 4: Past and future salvation

Janet carefully wrapped the loaf of warm bread in a towel and carried it the two blocks to Aunt Mary's home. (Aunt Mary was not truly a relative; but since none of her *real* relatives lived nearby, Janet had adopted her as her aunt.)

"Aunt Mary, here is a special treat from me to you. I baked it all by myself," said Janet.

"Well," said Aunt Mary, "there is only one thing to do—you sit down with me at my table, and we'll have a *tasting party*. We'll use your bread and my homemade strawberry jam. How does that sound to you?"

"Great!" said Janet.

As they shared the bread and jam together, Aunt Mary said: "Janet, your nice, warm bread reminds me of the last time our Lord Jesus ate with his disciples. As they shared the meal, none of them knew at the time Jesus would soon die on the cross. Do you

40

remember Pastor Beall describing how Jesus took a loaf of bread and broke it? He told the disciples that his own body would be broken like the bread. He also told them he would not eat it with them until he returned again."

"Aunt Mary," said Janet, "I know that when Jesus died on the cross, he took all my sin away. Since I have accepted Jesus as my Savior and Lord, joined the church, and was baptized, I take the Lord's Supper at church. I always thank Jesus for what he did for me. I shall never be afraid to die, because I know my sin is forgiven, forever and ever."

Aunt Mary said: "Yes, I know you have learned that fact well. May I tell you *another* part of the good news? When Jesus promised he would return again, he taught us that our salvation has a final part to it. In the *past*, he set us free from the punishment for our sin. As Jim learned from Mr. Robinson, *today* Jesus sets us free from the power Satan has over us. Now, I want to be sure you know that *in the future*, Jesus is going to set us free forever from the *presence of sin*."

"Does that mean there will be a time when we will not even be *able* to sin, Aunt Mary?"

"Yes," she replied. "We might think of it like this: do you remember when your father bought my car from me?"

Janet laughed. "Yes! He said you had the best used car he had ever seen. We enjoy riding in it so much!"

"Well, when he came to buy it, he gave me fifty dollars. I knew your father would bring the rest of the money to me on the day he promised to do so. Later, when that day came, he paid me as he promised. Janet, Jesus has promised us that the salvation we *now* have is only a first payment on what he is *going* to have for us. You see, our salvation in the future will include even more than we now have. Isn't that wonderful?"

FIND 1 PETER 1:3-5 IN YOUR BIBLE. USE IT TO UNSCRAMBLE THESE WORDS:

1. In verse 3, what did God give us by raising Jesus Christ from the dead?

EWN ELFI _____ _____

2. In verse 4, what is God keeping for us until he comes again?

CHRI SELSIBSGN _____ _____

3. Where are they kept for us?

NI EVNHAE ____ _____

In verse 5, what kind of salvation is promised:

salvation *past, present,* or *future?* _____

In verse 5, what keeps us safe while we wait for it?

G _ _ ' _   P _ _ _ _

WHY DO YOU THINK CHRISTIANS ARE NOT AFRAID OF DEATH?

_____

_____

_____

_____

_____

_____

_____

_____

_____

_____

Week 4: Three parts to salvation
Day 5: Review

FILL IN THE BLANKS ON THE PALM, THUMB, AND FINGER OF THE HAND DIAGRAM:

COMPLETE THIS PAGE BY YOURSELF. THEN SHOW IT TO YOUR PARENTS. YOU MAY HAVE A SPECIAL FRIEND WHO GAVE THIS SURVIVAL KIT TO YOU. IF SO, ALSO SHOW IT TO THAT PERSON.

DAILY DEVOTIONAL CHECKUP:

So far, twenty days of material have been provided in your SURVIVAL KIT, including today. If you have completed all twenty, circle that number below. If not, circle the number you have completed:

1   2   3   4   5   6   7   8   9   10   11
12   13   14   15   16   17   18   19   20

MY SCRIPTURE MEMORY

I can repeat the following verses from memory:
(Be prepared to share any, or all of them, if your parent asks you to do so.)

☐ PSALM 119:11   ☐ 1 CORINTHIANS 12:18
☐ ROMANS 6:14   ☐ 2 CORINTHIANS 5:17
☐ ROMANS 12:5   ☐ GALATIANS 5:22-23
☐ PHILIPPIANS 1:6   ☐ 1 CORINTHIANS 10:13

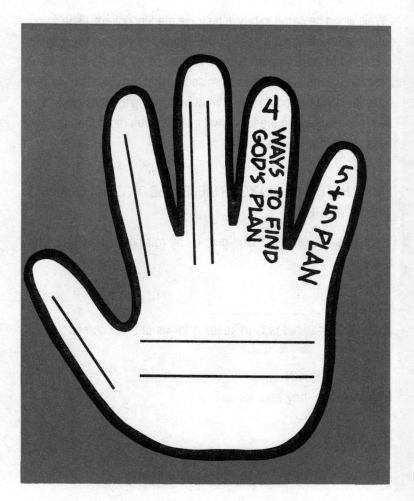

4 WAYS TO FIND GOD'S PLAN

5+5 PLAN

CAN YOU COMPLETE THE DIAGRAM MR. ROBINSON PUT ON THE CHALKBOARD?

(Look back to WEEK 4, DAY 1 if you cannot remember the diagram.)

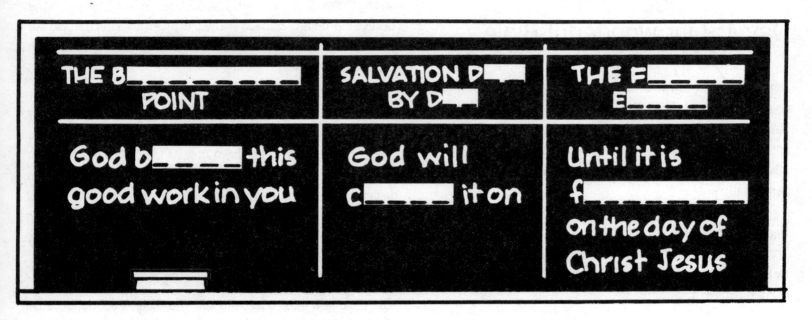

What is one thing Richard learned from standing on the ladder?

_____

_____

In your own words, explain for your parent the meaning of salvation *past*, *present*, and *future*.

ASK ONE OF YOUR PARENTS TO SIGN BELOW AFTER YOU HAVE SHOWN THEM TODAY'S REVIEW:

> I have reviewed the work my child has done this week.
>
> SIGNED:_____

Week 5: Four ways to find God's truth
Day 1: Our wonderful Bible

Janet and Jim received a letter addressed to them with a great deal of excitement. The letter was from the missionary they had heard at the church. He had returned to Thailand and had answered the letter they had written to him many weeks before. After admiring the beautiful stamp on the envelope, they opened it. Janet read:

Dear Janet and Jim,
Thank you for your letter. You have asked how people in Thailand try to find God. I will try to explain this to you. I have prepared a chart to explain it.

HERE ARE FOUR WAYS PEOPLE USE TO LEARN ABOUT GOD:

Man tries to learn about God through his feelings	Man tries to learn about God through men's ideas
Man tries to learn about God through his thoughts	Man tries to learn about God through the Bible

Here in Thailand, as in the United States, all four of these ways are used by some people. Many try to learn about God through their feelings, thoughts, or other men's ideas. In this country, many believe the ideas of Buddha will help them. In my letter, I would like to encourage *you* to accept the *BIBLE* as the right way. In fact, the Bible is the *only* way.

Jim and Janet, I will write out for you the words of 2 Timothy 3:15-17, from the *Good News Bible:* "You remember that ever since you were a child, you have known the Holy Scriptures, which are able to give you the wisdom that leads to salvation through faith in Christ Jesus. All Scripture is inspired by God and is useful for teaching the truth, rebuking error, correcting faults, and giving instruction for right living, so that the person who serves God may be fully qualified and equipped to do every kind of good deed."

Our Bible is a most unusual book. The Bible is special because God led men to write it. In the verses above, the word *inspired* is used. *Inspired* means God led men to write the record we call the Bible. No other book in all the world is like our Bible. It is the only one of its kind.

We know the Bible is true because by reading it we come to know the living God who has made himself known through his dealings with people in the past. But most important of all God made himself known in Jesus. The Bible is an inspired written record of God's making himself known to people. As we read it today, God's truth is made known to us. In fact, God makes *himself* known to us through Scripture.

Because the Bible is inspired by God, we know the three other ways people use to try to know God are not enough. *To truly know God, there is only one way.* That way is Jesus. Our wonderful Bible tells us about him.

Here in Thailand, the Bible is printed in the Thai language. I am glad it is, for we provide many Bibles for people who live here. I would like for you to pray for those who are just beginning to read this wonderful Bible here in Thailand. Pray that they will accept Jesus as their Lord.

I am glad you two, like Timothy, are learning what the Bible teaches. Thank you for writing me. Perhaps in four years, when I return again on furlough to the United States, I will meet you again.

Answer to Puzzle on Page 33

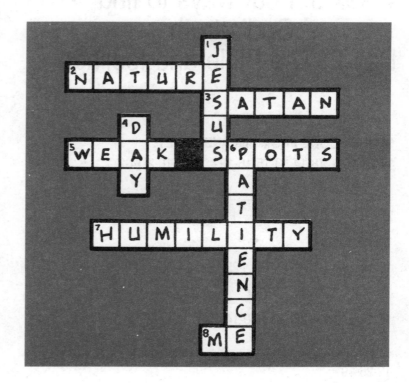

Week 5: Four ways to find God's truth
Day 2: The Bible and feelings

SECRET CODE FROM JIM AND JANET:

15-25-16   18-14-18-15-16-19   9-14-16-2-14-2

___ _____ _____

26-16-14   10-26-16-12   11-15

___ ____ __

16-14-18-14-18-8-14-16   25-13-5-14-2-2   23-14

_____ _____ __

16-14-9-22-14-23   11-10-14-18   14-9-14-16-19

_____ _____ __

12-26-19!

__ __!

When the church service was over, Jim and Janet waited until Pastor Beall had finished greeting the people at the door of the auditorium. "Hello there, twins!" he said. "I have not had a chance to visit with you recently. I am glad you waited to say *hello* to me."

"Pastor Beall," said Janet. "We would like to show you a letter we got from the missionary you invited to speak in our church."

The pastor read the letter carefully and then said: "He has given you some good answers. I would like to share some more about this with you. Why don't you come to visit me on Wednesday afternoon?"

The following Wednesday, the twins entered the pastor's office. Once again, Jim smelled the leather chairs and books. He decided he would have a room like this one in his house when he grew up—full of books.

"I would like to help you understand more about the chart in the missionary's letter. Let me begin by explaining that there are many people in our own country who depend on *feelings*, rather than the *Scripture*, to learn about God."

"Pastor Beall, do you think God speaks to people through dreams?" asked Janet. "Once we heard a lady say God had told her in a dream that our family should move to a different house."

"Janet, let's see what the Bible says about things like this, shall we? Let me read to you a part of Colossians 2:18-19: 'Do not allow yourselves to be condemned by anyone who claims to be superior because of special visions . . . . Such a person is all puffed up by his human way of thinking and has stopped holding on to Christ, who is the head of the body.'

"If someone tells you he has had a vision sent from God, how can you be certain that what he is saying is true? It is a dangerous thing to follow such advice. That's why God used the best way to tell men about himself. He gave us a written record of his truth."

Pastor Beall walked over to his bookshelf and took out a book. "The author of this book makes predictions about the future. I keep it only as an example of what we are talking about. It is an old book. The person who wrote it over a hundred years ago predicted the date that Jesus would return to the earth. Many people, believing this vision, sold their homes and waited for the exact hour he said Jesus would come. Of course, *we* know the man's feelings about this matter were not true. But the people who believed him did not know or did not believe Jesus' teaching."

Jim was looking for a verse in his Bible, and said: "Wow! I just read this verse yesterday in my daily devotions, Pastor Beall. Listen to Luke 12:40: 'And you, too, must be ready, because the Son of Man [Jesus] will come at an hour when you are not expecting him.' If those people had trusted what their Bibles said, they would not have been tricked by that man's vision."

QUESTIONS TO ANSWER

- The *best* source of truth is:

  — Experiences

  — The Bible

- Who are the "TWO MASTERS"?

  _____

  _____

- Who is a member of "the body of Christ"? To find out, complete this word:

  C H __ __ C H

Answer: "U R" ("You are")

Week 5: Four ways to find God's truth
Day 3: The Bible and thoughts

THE FIRST PARTS OF YOUR TWO MEMORY VERSES
FOR THIS WEEK APPEAR BELOW. WITH THIS HELP,
CAN YOU RECITE THEM?

"Whoever does not have the Spirit cannot . . ."

"For no prophetic message ever came . . ."

Pastor Beall placed the old book he had been showing to Jim and Janet back on the shelf. Reaching higher up, he selected a large book. "Twins, I used this book in college. It was my textbook for a class in philosophy. Do you know what the word *philosophy* means?"

Jim and Janet looked at each other, then back at the pastor. "No," said Jim. "We have no idea what it means."

"Well, let me explain," said Pastor Beall. "Through the centuries, people have tried to get understanding or wisdom. We call these

people *philosophers*—people who seek wisdom. Some philosophers are Christians; some are not. When philosophers and other people ignore the Bible, they try to find answers from other places. One thing I can tell you about all of them is this: thinking alone did not lead them to know God. Janet, will you read 1 Corinthians 1:19,25 for us?"

Janet read: "The scripture says, 'I will destroy the wisdom of the wise and set aside the understanding of the scholars. For what seems to be God's foolishness is wiser than human wisdom, and what seems to be God's weakness is stronger than human strength.' "

The pastor continued: "These verses do not teach that learning is wrong or not useful. Verse 19 teaches that people's thinking alone cannot lead them to know God. The good news is that salvation is a free gift of God. The cross means that God is known in the death of Jesus. The wisdom of God can only be received. The wisdom of God is not found in words people speak but in Christ. The death of Christ was not weakness and foolishness but God's power and wisdom."

"Pastor Beall," said Janet. "I think we understand now why we are memorizing 1 Corinthians 2:14 this week. It tells us that only *Christians* understand the real truth about God. Those who have not accepted Jesus often depend on their *own ideas.*"

Jim said, "I guess that's like one blind man trying to lead another blind man, isn't it?" He looked down at his Bible and said: "I am beginning to have a new love for our Bible. I can understand why you have spent so many years studying it, Pastor."

As he replaced the large philosophy book, the pastor said: "Of all the books I own, I have read only a few of them more than one time. I have even given away some books, because I knew I would never read them again." He reached over to his desk and picked up a Bible with a well-worn leather cover. "As you can see, *this* book is so worn that I will soon need to have a new cover put on it. I have read the same parts of the Bible dozens of times—and each time the Holy Spirit teaches me. Because the Bible contains the truth about God, no other book in the world is as important to us."

HOW MANY OF THE FOUR WAYS PEOPLE LEARN ABOUT GOD HAVE JIM AND JANET LEARNED ABOUT SO FAR? (Underline your answers.)

FEELINGS   MEN'S IDEAS
THOUGHTS   THE BIBLE

READ 1 CORINTHIANS 2:8. BECAUSE RULERS DID NOT UNDERSTAND OR ACCEPT WHO JESUS WAS, WHAT DID THEY DO TO HIM?

_____

_____

_____

_____

_____

_____

Week 5: Four ways to find God's truth
Day 4: The Bible and men's ideas

Jim leaned back in the leather chair in Pastor Beall's office. He was thinking about the many mornings through the years he had seen his father reading his Bible. His dad also learned truth from God's book. Silently he prayed: "Lord Jesus, I want to be like my dad and Pastor Beall. I thank you for my Bible. I promise you now that I will never stop having my devotional time. I want to grow up knowing all I can about you."

Pastor Beall's secretary entered the room with a tray of glasses filled with lemonade. As they drank it, Pastor Beall said: "There's one more part to the chart the missionary sent to you. I want to read a few verses to you from Matthew 15." Jim and Janet listened carefully as he read: "Then some Pharisees and teachers of the Law came from Jerusalem to Jesus and asked him, Why is it that your disciples disobey the teaching handed down by our ances-

tors?" The pastor said: "In this verse, Jesus faced a serious problem. Many people think the way to know God is to keep on doing things because our ancestors did them. This can be a good and important thing to do—but in *this* case, the Pharisees put more importance on what their ancestors taught than what the Old Testament taught. Later in this chapter, in verse 9, Jesus quotes Isaiah, who said, 'It is no use for them to worship me, because they teach man-made rules as though they were my laws!'

"Twins, there are those in *our* day who believe the way to know God is by keeping rules made by people long ago. In doing so, they do not use the Bible, or they no longer use the Bible alone to learn what God has said to us. People who obey men's rules are trying very hard to find God, but they will not succeed. You see, rules made by people now or by people who lived long ago cannot be substituted for what God has made known to us through Jesus."

Janet looked puzzled. "I don't think I understand, Pastor. Could you give me an example of what you mean?"

The pastor thought for a moment and said: "There are dozens of examples I could give you. For instance, some believe that sprinkling a baby will cause the baby to go to heaven when he or she dies. No Scripture teaches anything like that. Each one of us must *personally* receive Jesus Christ into his or her life. That *is* taught in the Bible. Ideas of people long ago—not Scripture—is the reason babies are sprinkled in some churches."

Janet said: "Now I understand. Pastor, it is important to be sure our beliefs come *only* from the Bible, isn't it?"

"Yes it is, Janet. And it is important that we do not substitute man-made beliefs for truths God gave us in the Bible. This is *another* reason why it's important for you and Jim to have daily devotional times. The more you study the Bible, the more you will be protected against the three *wrong* ways people try to find God's truth."

BELOW ARE EXAMPLES OF WAYS PEOPLE TRY TO FIND GOD'S TRUTH
Write one of these four words in each blank, indicating which way is being used:
FEELINGS THOUGHTS PEOPLE'S IDEAS THE BIBLE

_____ Mary is memorizing Scripture.

_____ George is reading a book by a philosopher.

_____ Phil has had a vision while he was sleeping.

_____ Diane is following man-made rules.

WHAT WOULD YOU SUGGEST TO GEORGE, PHIL, AND DIANE?_____

_____

_____

Week 5: Four ways to find God's truth
Day 5: Review

COMPLETE THIS PAGE BY YOURSELF. THEN SHOW IT TO YOUR PARENTS. YOU MAY HAVE A SPECIAL FRIEND WHO GAVE THIS SURVIVAL KIT TO YOU. IF SO, ALSO SHOW IT TO THAT PERSON.

DAILY DEVOTIONAL CHECKUP:

So far, there have been twenty-five days of material provided in your SURVIVAL KIT, including today. If you have completed all twenty-five days, circle that number below. If not, circle the number of days you have completed:

1 2 3 4 5 6 7 8 9 10
11 12 13 14 15 16 17 18 19 20
21 22 23 24 25

MY SCRIPTURE MEMORY

I can repeat the following verses from memory:
(Be prepared to quote those you check if your parent or friend asks you to do so.)

☐ PSALM 119:11   ☐ 1 CORINTHIANS 12:18

☐ ROMANS 6:14   ☐ 2 CORINTHIANS 5:17
☐ ROMANS 12:5   ☐ GALATIANS 5:22-23
☐ PHILIPPIANS 1:6   ☐ 1 CORINTHIANS 10:13
☐ 1 CORINTHIANS 2:14   ☐ 2 PETER 1:21

FILL IN THE BLANKS ON THE PALM, THUMB, AND FINGERS OF THE HAND DIAGRAM:

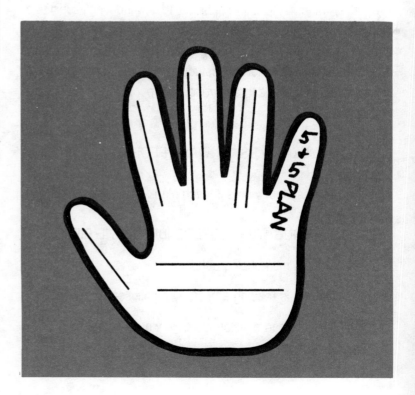

CAN YOU COMPLETE THIS CHART WITHOUT LOOKING AT THE PREVIOUS PAGES IN YOUR BOOK?

HERE ARE FOUR WAYS PEOPLE USE TO LEARN ABOUT GOD:

People try to learn about God through their feelings	People try to learn about God through ideas
People try to learn about God through thoughts	People try to learn about God through the Bible

IN YOUR OWN WORDS, TELL YOUR PARENTS WHAT YOU HAVE LEARNED THIS WEEK ABOUT THE FOUR WAYS PEOPLE USE TO FIND GOD'S TRUTH. EXPLAIN WHY THE BIBLE IS THE ONLY RIGHT WAY.

ASK ONE OF YOUR PARENTS TO SIGN BELOW AFTER YOU HAVE COMPLETED THIS REVIEW.

I have reviewed the work my child has done this week. SIGNED:_____

TRY THIS
Use the names of these Bible books to fill in the puzzle:
ACTS, MARK, 1 CORINTHIANS, MATTHEW, LUKE

```
     _ _ T _ _ _ _
     _ _ R _
       _ U _ _
     _ _ T _
_ _ _ _ _ _ _ H _ _ _ _
```

Week 6: The five-and-five plan
Day 1: Who needs Jesus?

These friends are open to my sharing Christ	These friends are not open to my sharing Christ
1. Susan	1. Georgia
2. Terry	2. Mildred
3. Bonita	3. Debbie
4. Sharon	4. Mrs. Bannister
5. Margaret	5. Ethel

Dad and Mother were still asleep. Janet and Jim, as usual, had prepared their own Saturday morning breakfast. After they had eaten, they tiptoed back to their bedrooms for their devotionals. Janet read a booklet given to her by Aunt Mary. It encouraged her to write down the names of ten friends who had not yet become Christians. Janet took a sheet of notebook paper and wrote down the names of ten friends at school.

The booklet then instructed Janet to divide the names into two groups. In the *first group*, Janet listed those she could tell how she became a Christian. In the *second group*, she listed those she felt she could *not* talk to about Jesus.

"Look, Jim," Janet said as she walked into his room. "I have made a list." She showed him the page:

"Hmmm," said Jim. "You have exactly five for each group, don't you? You could call them THE FIVE-AND-FIVE PEOPLE, couldn't you?"

"Jim, that's a *great* idea. I'll do that. I'll have a FIVE-AND-FIVE PLAN. I'm going to my room to go on reading the booklet. Maybe it will tell me what to do about the five on my list who are *not* open to my telling them about Christ. Did you notice I put my teacher, Mrs. Bannister, on the list? I can tell by the way she talks to us in class that she doesn't believe in Jesus. I don't think she would let *me* talk to her, but how I wish she might accept Jesus as Lord."

Janet continued to read the booklet. She discovered it did give her a suggestion about those she could not talk to about her new faith.

It recommended she *pray* for them every day. This verse was quoted: "In all your prayers ask God for what you need, always asking him with a thankful heart" (Philippians 4:6).

The booklet also suggested that she should learn how to share the news that she had accepted Jesus as her Lord. "I see," Janet said to herself. "The *first* five, I will *tell* that I have decided to trust in Jesus. The *second* five, I'll add to my prayer list. That will be my FIVE-AND-FIVE PLAN."

SECRET MESSAGE FROM JANET TO YOU:

13-15-23   5-22-2-11   19-15-25-16   "3-22-9-14

‾ ‾ ‾   ‾ ‾ ‾ ‾ ‾   ‾ ‾ ‾ ‾   " ‾ ‾ ‾ ‾ ‾

26-13-12   3-22-9-14."

‾ ‾ ‾   ‾ ‾ ‾ ‾."

These friends are open to my sharing Christ	These friends are not open to my sharing Christ
1.	1.
2.	2.
3.	3.
4.	4.
5.	5.

REMEMBER, WITH FIVE YOU CAN SHARE YOUR TESTIMONY; WITH THE OTHER FIVE YOU CAN PRAY FOR THEIR SALVATION.

Week 6: The five-and-five plan
Day 2: Prepare your testimony

BEFORE READING TODAY'S MATERIAL, READ MATTHEW 10:32-33.

Janet took out a sheet of notebook paper. Her booklet showed her how to prepare her testimony. The booklet said that Acts 9:1-22 and Acts 22:3-15 told how Paul became a Christian. These passages told about:
1. PAUL'S LIFE BEFORE HE BECAME A CHRISTIAN
2. HOW PAUL REALIZED HE NEEDED CHRIST
3. HOW PAUL BECAME A CHRISTIAN
4. HOW JESUS HELPED PAUL IN HIS DAILY LIFE

Janet decided to write out her own testimony. This is what she wrote:
MY LIFE BEFORE I BECAME A CHRISTIAN:
Before I became a Christian, I told lies. I cheated when I played games with my friends. One time I took money from my mother's purse. I felt bad about many things I did. I wanted to please myself more than I wanted to please God. I knew something was wrong between God and me.

HOW I REALIZED I NEEDED CHRIST:
I knew I had sinned. I knew I was not right with God. I wanted to change. My father explained to me that I needed to give my life to Jesus. But I had to trust Jesus as my Savior because I wanted to with all my heart. Jesus would not force me to give myself to him.

HOW I BECAME A CHRISTIAN:
One night, my mother was talking to me about what being a Christian meant. I began to understand that it meant I would let Jesus become Lord of my life. It meant trusting and obeying him. I told my mother I wanted to pray that night to invite Jesus Christ to live in my life. I wanted him to forgive me of my sin. We prayed together. When we finished, I knew that Jesus had heard me and had forgiven me. Later, I was baptized with my twin brother, Jim. Jesus commanded each person who believes to be baptized. Baptism is a way to confess faith in Jesus.

HOW JESUS HELPS ME IN MY DAILY LIFE:
Now, when I am tempted to do something wrong or say something wrong, I know Jesus is with me; and I ask him to help me. He helps me not to lie and not to cheat. I am kind to my brother, Jim. I love Jesus more than anybody or anything in the world. He died for me, and I love him with all my heart.

NOW IT'S YOUR TURN!

In the space below, write out *your* testimony. Use only words a person who is not a Christian would understand.

MY LIFE BEFORE RECEIVING CHRIST

_____

_____

_____

_____

_____

_____

HOW I REALIZED I NEEDED CHRIST

_____

_____

_____

_____

_____

HOW I BECAME A CHRISTIAN

_____

_____

_____

_____

_____

_____

HOW CHRIST HELPS ME IN MY DAILY LIFE

_____

_____

_____

_____

_____

NOW, PLAN TO SHARE YOUR TESTIMONY WITH THE FIVE ON YOUR LIST WITH WHOM YOU CAN TALK ABOUT CHRIST.

Week 6: The five-and-five plan
Day 3: Prepare your prayer list

When Janet finished writing her testimony, she walked back into Jim's room and asked him to listen while she shared it with him. He was pleased and asked for her help so that he, too, might prepare his testimony. When he finished, *she* listened to *him.* By then, their parents had awakened, and the twins both shared their testimonies with them.

Later that morning, Janet wrote the names of five people on her prayer list. She also underlined 1 Timothy 2:3,4,8 in her Bible.

(WOULD YOU DO THAT, TOO? *RIGHT NOW.* UNDERLINE THOSE VERSES IN *YOUR* BIBLE. THINK OF THE MEANING OF EACH VERSE AS YOU UNDERLINE IT.)

Dad walked by and said, "Lollipop, what are you doing?"

She said: "I am writing on my prayer list the names of the five people I am going to pray for. One of them is my teacher, Dad. I think the only thing I can do is to pray for her. I surely hope it will help her come to accept Jesus."

Dad put his hand on her shoulder: "Janet, do you know what prayer does? It invites Jesus to use his power to meet a great need. That's why your prayer is just as important as the prayers of someone like Pastor Beall. The answer to your prayer doesn't depend on how old you are or how long you have been a Christian—*it depends on the power that Jesus has.* In Matthew 17:20, Jesus said that even faith as small as a mustard seed is enough to move mountains. So, don't ever feel that your prayers are not important. *They are,* and you will discover for yourself that God does answer them. Of course, when you pray for people's salvation, you ought to remember that God does not force anybody to be saved."

After he left the room, Janet softly closed the door. She sat at her desk and prayed: "Dear Lord Jesus, Mrs. Bannister looked like she had been crying when she came to school yesterday. She never speaks about *you* in any way. I guess she must be unhappy. I know you bring happiness to every person who lets you come to live in their lives. I pray, Lord, that you will help me find a way to tell her of your great love for her. In your name I pray, Amen."

YOU MUST FIND OUT FOR YOURSELF THAT GOD WILL ANSWER *YOUR* PRAYER FOR OTHERS. BEGIN TO PRAY FOR *YOUR* FIVE NOW.

READ JAMES 1:5-8 IN YOUR BIBLE.

As you think about praying for the salvation of your friends, do these verses teach you an important fact?

Underline the fact you know these verses teach:

I just pray and hope for the best.

Praying really doesn't make any difference.

I should pray in faith, believing that my prayer will make a difference.

If I cannot tell others about Jesus, nothing else I can do will help them accept Jesus as their Savior and Lord.

Did you underline the third sentence? That was the right answer, wasn't it? *How can you pray with greater faith?* One way is to *see* the person you pray for in the way they will be after your prayer has been answered. For example, Janet could pray for Mrs. Bannister, seeing her as a *happy* person, showing by her new life that Jesus has brought answers to her problems.

TURN TO YOUR PRAYER LIST ON PAGE 11. ADD THE NAMES OF THE FIVE PEOPLE YOU WANT TO PRAY FOR, AND SPEND SOME TIME THIS MORNING PRAYING FOR THEM BY NAME. YOUR LORD *DOES* ANSWER PRAYER.

JONES:.

Week 6: The five-and-five plan
Day 4: It works!

"Mother! Mother!" cried Janet, running into the house with her school books and her lunch box. "I have so much to tell you. I shared my testimony with two of the five on my list today. One of them was Terry. Guess what she said? She told me that before they moved here, she and her sister used to go to church. She had almost decided to become a Christian before they moved. She told me that for the past few days she has wanted to find a new church. Last Sunday she felt badly to be staying home. When I shared my testimony, she told me she really was interested. Mother, may I ask her to spend Friday night with me? You can help her as you helped me when I accepted Jesus."

Mother looked lovingly at Janet. "Of *course* you may invite her, dear. I am so happy that Terry is thinking about accepting Jesus. I prayed for you today as I did my housework. I think God was answering *both* our prayers."

"Mother, there's *more*! I got to school a little early this morning; and when I entered my room, I saw Mrs. Bannister reading a little book. I took my report up to give to her, and I saw that she was

reading a small New Testament. She did not want to talk about it, I guess, because she put it in her desk drawer when I saw it. But, Mother, I truly believe that God is answering my prayer for her. I know if she reads much of the Bible, she will learn Jesus has died for her and that he wants to give her a new life."

Mother brought a plate of cookies and a glass of milk to the table just as Jim entered the room. Quickly, she poured another glass as Janet retold the events of the day to Jim. When she finished, Jim did not say anything at all. Janet did not understand why he was quiet and wanted to ask him about it.

Jim finally spoke: "Janet, it has happened *again* to us. You remember I wanted us to become Christians *together*, and you accepted Jesus two weeks before I did. Well, I wanted to give *my* testimony today, as you have done. But somehow I didn't have the courage, I guess. Now, instead of our both starting to share our faith on the same day, you are ahead of me again. I know that my friends may not hear about Jesus from any other person if I do not tell them about him. I know what I must do. Janet, I am going to pray that Jesus will give me the courage to talk about him tomorrow."

Mother said: "Jim, I would not worry about trying to keep up with Janet. Instead, just ask the Lord to give you the right time with the right friend to talk about him. When it *is* the right time, you won't have to worry about having the courage. I honestly don't think you need more *courage*, Jim. You're not a coward. Instead, just tell our Lord you are ready to speak when he opens the way for you to do so. You will be surprised to learn how easily you will share your faith when he is guiding you."

"Thanks, Mom," said Jim. "That makes sense. From now on, I am going to pray each morning in my devotional time for Jesus to show me the *right time* to share my testimony. Then, when it *is* the right time, I will do it."

WILL YOU PRAY THAT WAY, TOO? ALL JESUS WANTS IS FOR US TO BE *WILLING* TO SHARE OUR FAITH. LEAVE THE REST TO HIM.

Week 6: The five-and-five plan
Day 5: Review

YOUR LAST DAY! AREN'T YOU PLEASED THAT YOU HAVE MEMORIZED ALL THE VERSES AND COMPLETED ALL THE WORK IN YOUR SURVIVAL KIT? NOW, COMPLETE THIS PAGE BY YOURSELF. SHOW IT TO YOUR PARENT AND PERHAPS ALSO TO YOUR SPECIAL FRIEND.

DAILY DEVOTIONAL CHECKUP:

With today, you should have completed thirty days of material provided in your SURVIVAL KIT. If you have completed all thirty days, put an *X* in this box: ☐

If you have not, on the line below list the days you have missed:

_____

ARE THERE ANY SCRIPTURE VERSES YOU *CANNOT* REPEAT FROM MEMORY? IF SO, PLACE AN *X* BESIDE THE VERSES YOU HAVE NOT YET MEMORIZED:

☐ PSALM 119:11   ☐ 2 CORINTHIANS 5:17

☐ 1 CORINTHIANS 12:18   ☐ ROMANS 12:5
☐ ROMANS 6:14   ☐ GALATIANS 5:22-23
☐ PHILIPPIANS 1:6   ☐ 1 CORINTHIANS 10:13
☐ 1 CORINTHIANS 2:14   ☐ 2 PETER 1:21
☐ MATTHEW 7:7-8   ☐ ROMANS 1:16

FILL IN THE BLANKS ON THE PALM, THUMB, AND FINGERS OF THE HAND DIAGRAM:

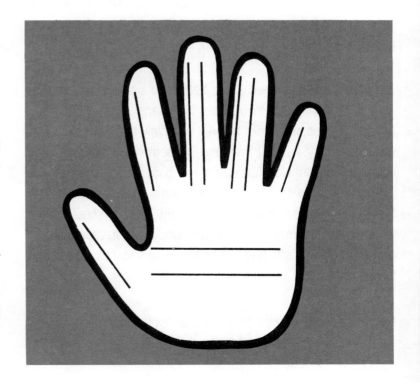

REPORT TO MY PARENT

During the past month, I have learned many new things. I always want to remember these special facts:

(*You may review any part of your SURVIVAL KIT as you prepare this report to your parent(s). List below, from your days of study, the things which have helped you the most. Discuss them with your parents.*)

FROM WEEK 1, *MY NEW LIFE,* I LEARNED . . .

_____

_____

_____

FROM WEEK 2, *ONE BODY,* I LEARNED . . .

_____

_____

_____

FROM WEEK 3, *TWO MASTERS,* I LEARNED . . .

_____

_____

_____

FROM WEEK 4, *THREE PARTS TO SALVATION,* I LEARNED . . .

_____

_____

_____

FROM WEEK 5, *FOUR WAYS TO FIND GOD'S TRUTH,* I LEARNED . . .

_____

_____

_____

FROM WEEK 6, *THE FIVE-AND-FIVE PLAN,* I LEARNED . . .

_____

_____

_____

I have reviewed the work my child has done this week.

SIGNED:_____

A Message to Parents

You may rightly expect your church to provide your child with basic Bible training. Facts about God can be so acquired, *but most of your child's personal values will be acquired at home.* There is a critical question, therefore, you will want to answer for yourself: *HOW MUCH RESPONSIBILITY CAN I AFFORD TO TURN OVER TO OTHERS FOR THE SPIRITUAL DEVELOPMENT OF MY CHILD?*

Without a parent's strong convictions to guide the child, proper decisions will not be made about what *is*, and what is *not*, valuable in life.

Some parents say, I won't force religious beliefs on my child. The danger of this approach is that a passive attitude toward faith may cause the child to think: God is an option. I can take him or leave him. He is not really important.

Therefore, it is important for your own deep convictions about God to be shared with your child. Your positive encouragement toward the completion of this material will cause good habits to begin.

When your child approaches you with the weekly REVIEW, your attention to the material will show that you value what your child is doing.

As a parent, you may or may not have made your own decision to accept Jesus Christ as Lord. Either way, you do not need to be an expert to encourage your child. Simply take an interest in the reviewing of each week's work. It's honest to say: I don't know all the answers. I'll help wherever I can. Maybe we'll learn some things together.

If you desire, you may secure a copy of the *Adult* version of this SURVIVAL KIT FOR NEW CHRISTIANS from your church. You would then be studying, on a more mature level, what your child is studying.

When your child is in the turbulent teens, faced with peer pressure, you will be happy you invested this time of value giving. We trust this SURVIVAL KIT will draw you and your child closer than you have ever been before.

Ask your church to order billfold-size cards from your state Church Training department to recognize children who complete this study.